T ... ng Mixture

by Tony Bradman
Illustrated by Bill Ledger

OXFORD

UNIVERSITY PRESS

In this story ...

Ben

Ben can run fast. He is as fast as lightning.

Pip

Mrs Molten

Magnus

Mrs Molten has set a test for the class. They need to mix the powders.

Ben is not sure of the mixture.

Ben frowns. The clear mixture is getting darker.

Did I spoil it with all that powder?

The mixture boils. Then it fizzes.

The mixture splashes on Mrs Molten.

Mrs Molten floats up in the air!

Ben gasps. "She is near the roof."

"How are we going to get her down?"
Pip yells.

I will
get help.

Ben runs down the stairs at lightning speed.

"Magnus, you need to bring the ladder now!" yells Ben.

They run to the classroom.

Mrs Molten tells Ben how to mix a cure.

Ben darts up with the cure.

Mrs Molten gets down the ladder.

"Did I pass the test?" Ben checks.
Mrs Molten grins. "Yes ... in the end!"

Retell the story ...

1

2

3

4

5

6